Draw a honey pot on each shelf.

Color the box red that is for Piglet. Color the boxes yellow that are for Pooh.

How many times can you find the word HONEY in the puzzle? Look up, down, forwards, and backwards.

```
Y  H  Y  E  N  O  H  Y
H  O  N  E  Y  N  O  H
H  O  E  N  Y  E  N  Y
O  H  Y  O  O  N  E  E
N  N  O  Y  N  H  Y  N
E  H  O  N  E  Y  E  O
Y  O  H  Y  E  N  H  H
```

© Disney

What is Pooh thinking about? Draw a picture of it in the bubble.

Can you find 3 bees?

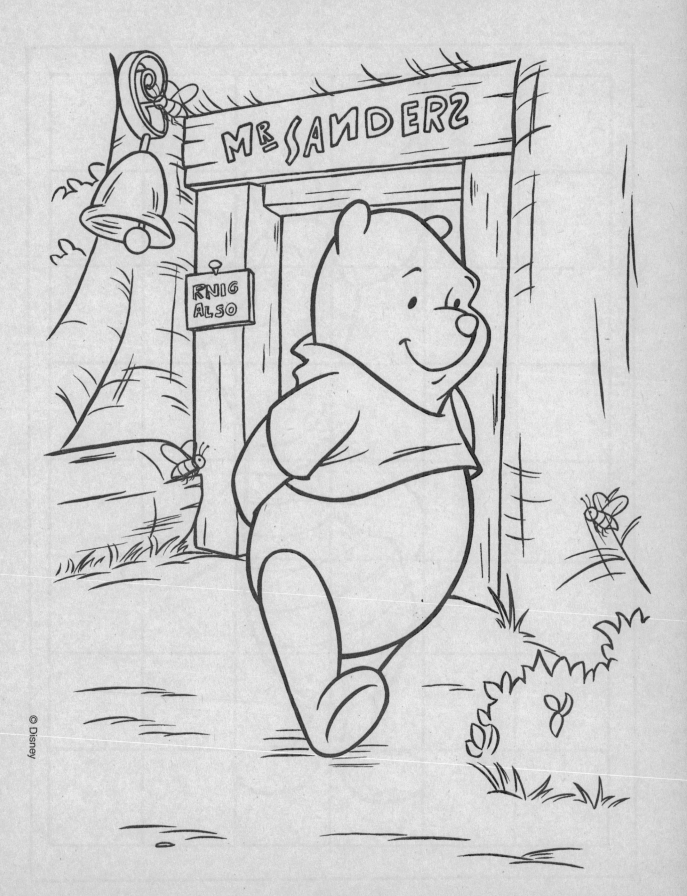

Use the picture as a guide to draw Piglet on the next page.

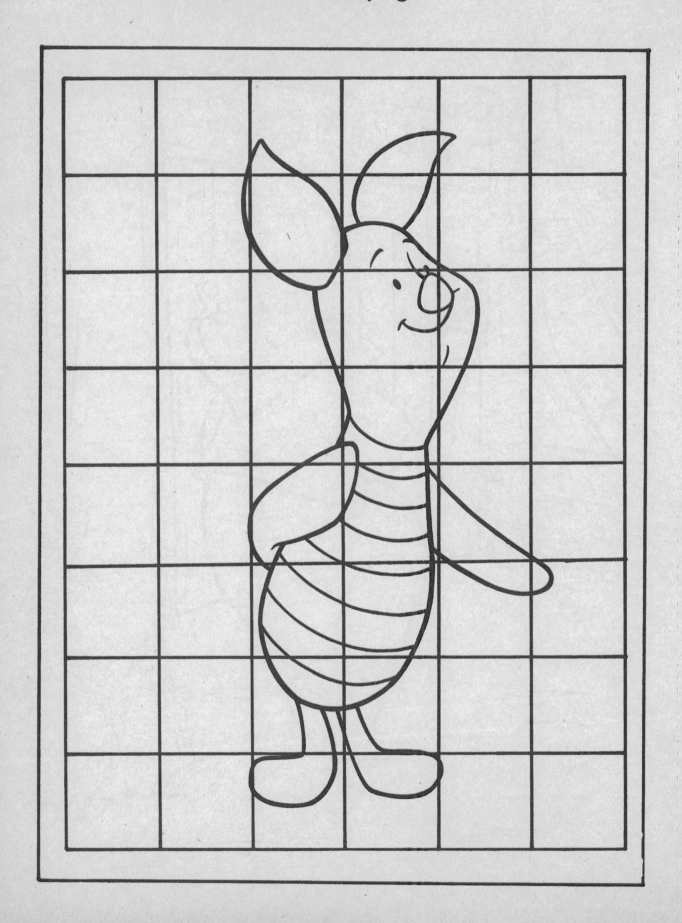

Use the picture as a guide to draw Piglet on the next page.

Can you lead Pooh to Kanga and Roo's house?

Decorate Roo's jar.

What kind of animal is Eeyore? To find out, follow the lines leading from each letter to an empty box. Write the letters in the boxes.

N O Y D K E

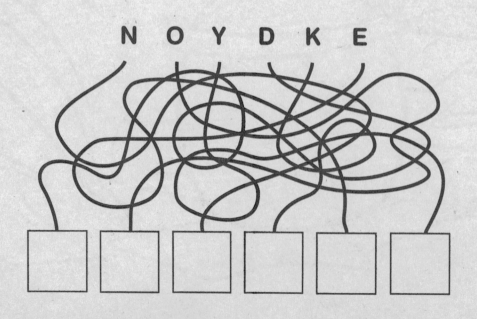

Use your crayons to decorate a new ribbon for Eeyore's tail.

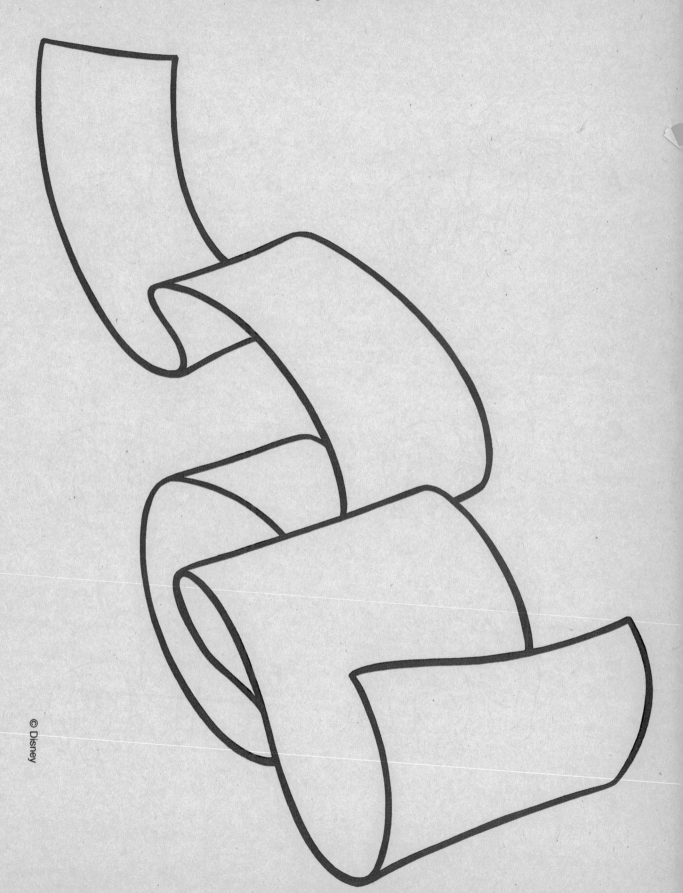

Find the one that is different.

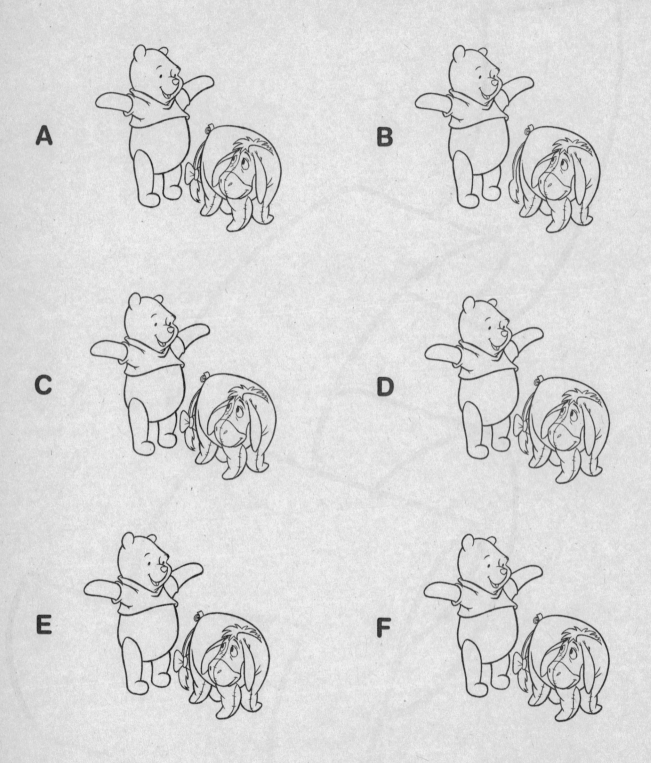

A

B

C

D

E

F

Can you find 3 carrots hiding in this picture?

Look up, down, forwards, and backwards to find the vegetable names cabbage, spinach, carrot, radish, and tomato in the puzzle.

```
E L T O M A T O W
D C E L D S H C I
C A B B A G E P S
M R I Y R H A N L
A R S B P C A C E
L O W N F A B S Z
R T P E R N Y E B
A D K H S I D A R
N E S B L P O I T
A R G N B S C R N
```

Draw lines to match the packets of seeds.

What would you grow in the garden?
Draw some vegetables, flowers, or fruit.

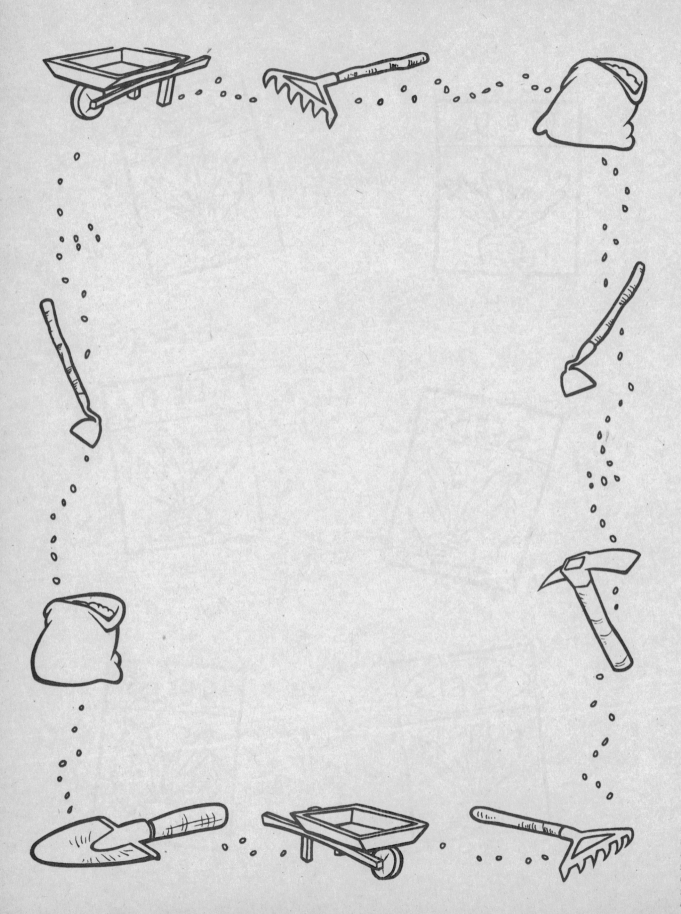

Which friend is Pooh going to visit? To find out, cross out the letters that appear 3 times or more. Write the remaining letters in order on the lines.

D T A S L

I S L D A

S A G D G

D E R S L

_ _ _ _ _ _

Honey Pot Game (a game for two or more players)

Take turns drawing a straight line between any two dots to make a square. When you make a square, put your initials in it and take another turn. Count 1 point for empty squares, and 2 points for squares with Pooh or a honey pot. When all of the dots have been connected, the player with the most points wins.

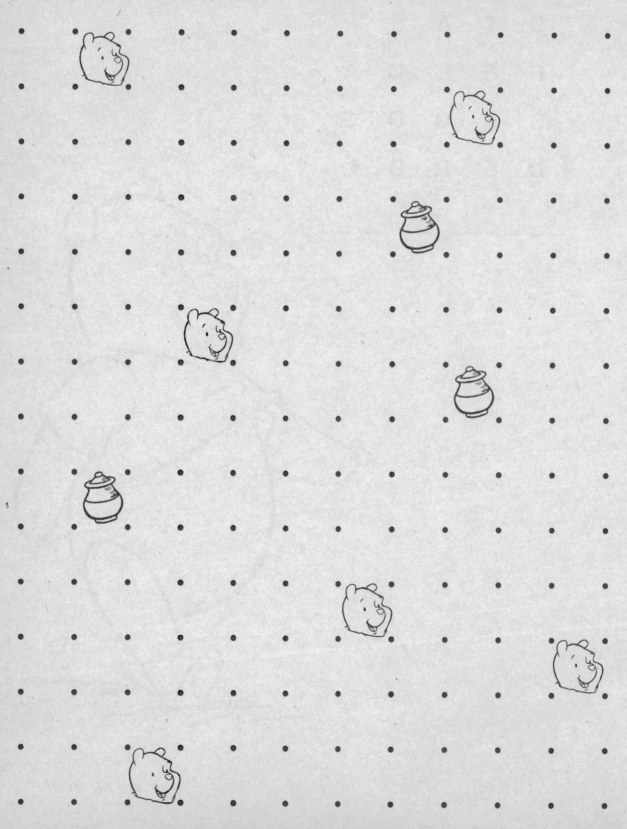

Play the Honey Pot Game AGAIN!

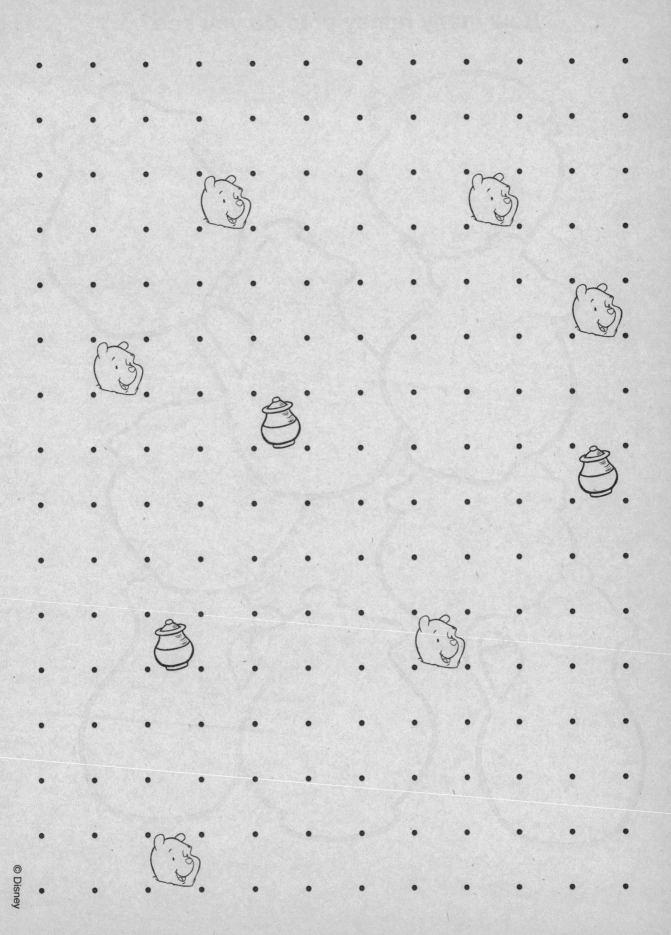

How many honey pots do you see?

Color the picture. Have a grown-up help you cut out the pieces along the dotted lines. Try putting them back together.

Color the picture. Paste it and the stand to a piece of cardboard. Have a grown-up help you cut them out. Tape the stand to the back of the picture. Place the picture in a special place.

Tape to back of picture.

Fold along dashed line.

HUNI

© Disney

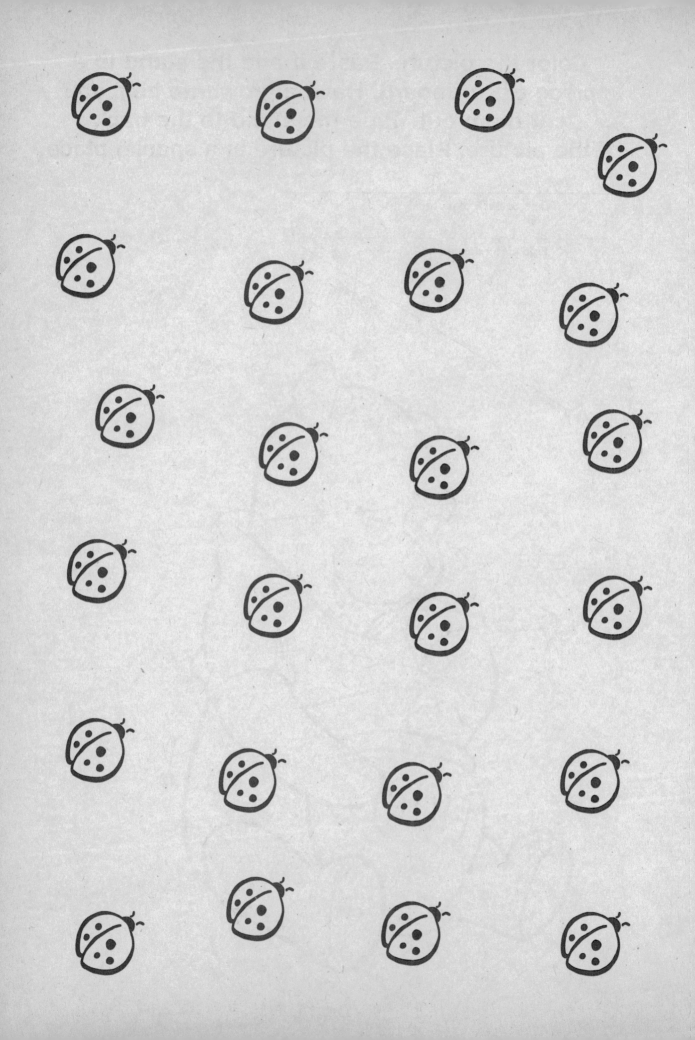

What is Pooh pulling?
Connect the dots to find out.

© Disney

Connect the dots to see what Pooh wants to eat.

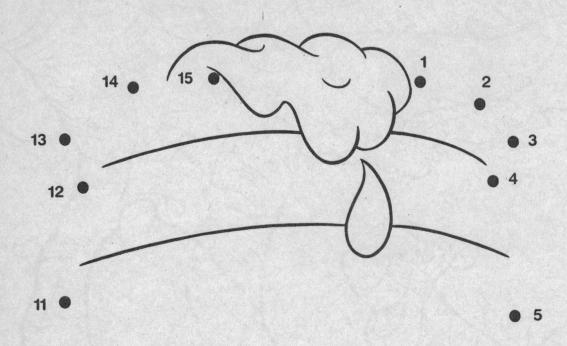

14   15

13

12

11

10

1

2

3

4

5

6

9   8   7

Color the flowers with 4 petals red.
Color the flowers with 6 petals yellow.

Tigger bounces and springs in lots of directions. Which picture looks like his shadow?

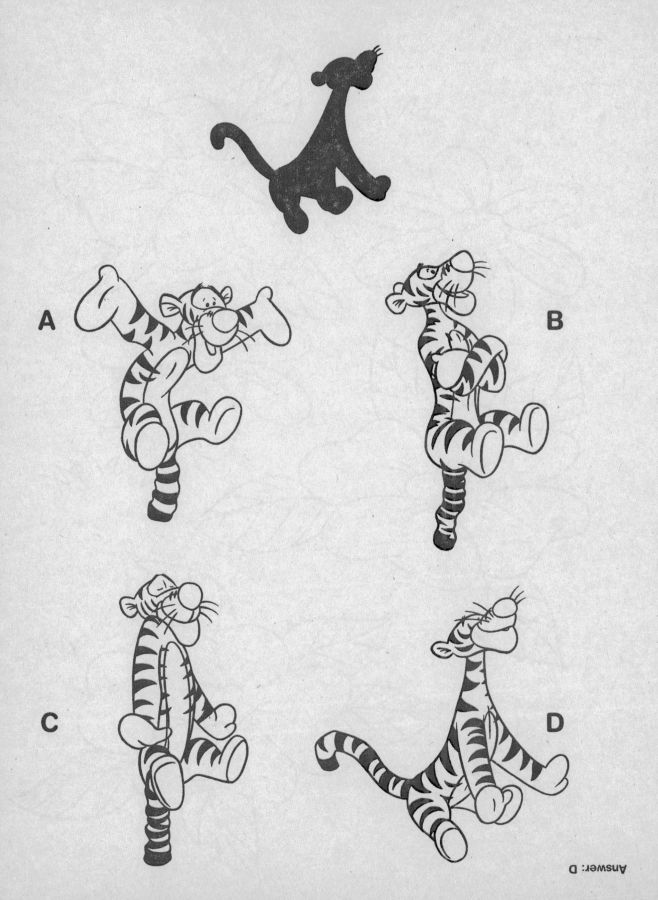

A

B

C

D

Who lives in the Hundred-Acre Wood? Look up, down, across, backwards, and forwards to find their names in the puzzle.

EEYORE   PIGLET

POOH   OWL

RABBIT   ROO   TIGGER

A	R	E	R	O	Y	E	E
T	I	G	G	E	R	O	G
S	D	O	T	N	A	S	P
E	Y	R	P	Y	B	E	I
S	B	O	D	G	B	Y	G
B	Y	O	E	T	I	I	L
H	O	O	P	U	T	W	E
H	G	G	A	P	O	L	T

Answer:

© Disney

Look carefully at the pictures on these two pages.
How many differences can you find?

Answer: Differences are candlestick on stool; pattern on rug; picture; direction Roo is facing; missing ball on bed post.

Lead Rabbit to Kanga and Roo's house.

HUNNY

© Disney

HUNNY

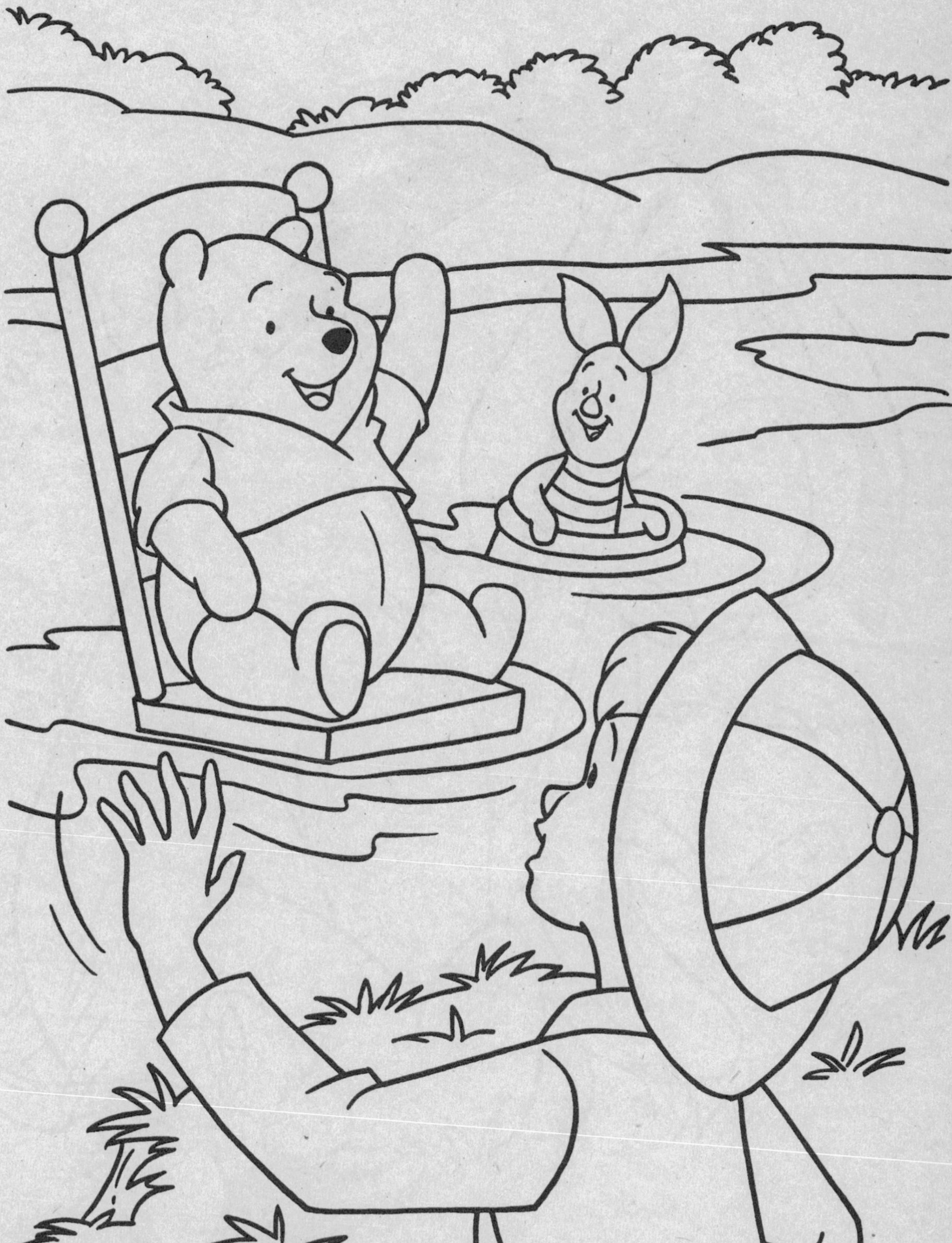